Letterland

Grammar

Activity Book 1

Sentence punctuation

This book belongs to:

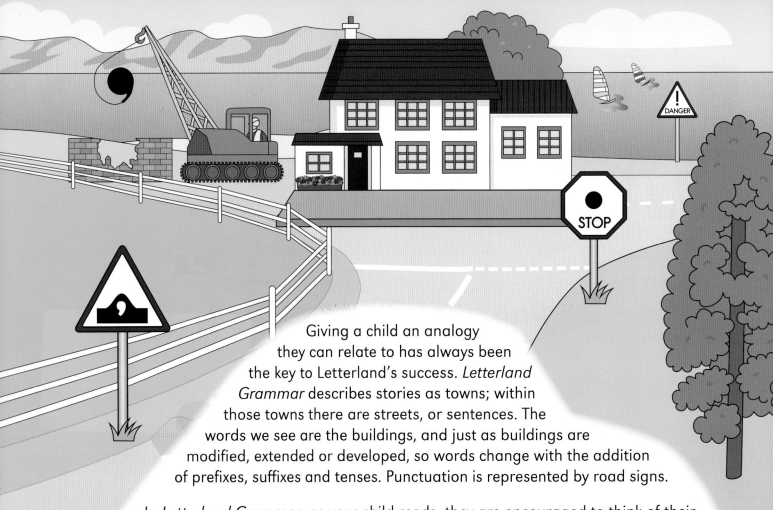

Giving a child an analogy they can relate to has always been the key to Letterland's success. *Letterland Grammar* describes stories as towns; within those towns there are streets, or sentences. The words we see are the buildings, and just as buildings are modified, extended or developed, so words change with the addition of prefixes, suffixes and tenses. Punctuation is represented by road signs.

In *Letterland Grammar*, as your child reads, they are encouraged to think of their finger on the page as a car travelling along a street looking out for 'reading' signs along the way. Use the 'Little car' finger puppet to bring this idea to life!

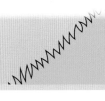

Stop, look, listen!
Read through these sections with your child. It's important that the concept is introduced clearly first.

Get set
These are examples to work through together slowly. Give your child support and encouragement as they complete the activities.

Go!
Encourage your child to have a go at these activities on their own.

Contents of Activity Book 1

Just as road signs tell car drivers how to behave on the roads, punctuation enables readers to successfully navigate sentences and paragraphs. This book introduces sentences and explains how punctuation helps a reader to understand meaning.

Stop, look, listen!

Just as buildings sit in rows to make a street, so words work together to make sentences.

The start of a sentence

The first building in a street is special. It is often 'Number 1'. The first word of a sentence is special too. It uses a capital letter to draw attention to itself and show how special it is.

The end of a sentence

Full stops are like 'stop' signs. They tell us that we are at the end of a sentence and must stop before we start reading the next one.

The cat ran up the tree.

Get set...

Trace the **capital letter** at the start of each of these sentences.
Put a **full stop** at the end too.

Look in the big box

They went to the park with dad

I like to play with my toys

4

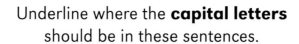

Underline where the **capital letters** should be in these sentences.

it is Jack's birthday soon. he is going to be seven years old. his mum is planning a party. all of his friends are going to go.

Use **full stops** to show where these sentences end.

Jack's dad has booked the village hall for his party His mum has made a cake Jack needs to invite his friends He is very excited

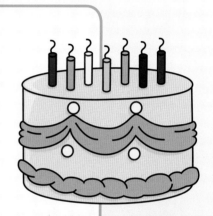

Write three sentences about your last birthday.
Remember to start each with a **capital letter** and end with a **full stop**.

Jack has written a birthday party invitation, but he has forgotten to start each sentence with a **capital letter** or finish it with a **full stop**. Use your stickers to correct it.

STICKER TIME!

PARTY TIME!

to Katie

you are invited to my birthday party   it is on Sunday at 4pm in the village hall   there will be lots of cake and ice cream and the best magic show ever the party will finish at 6 o'clock let   my mum know if you can come   i hope you can

from Jack

Which reply should Katie send to Jack? Tick the box.

to Jack
i would love to come to your party. see you on Sunday.
from Katie

To Jack
I would love to come to your party. See you on Sunday.
From Katie

To Jack
I would love to come to your party See you on Sunday
from Katie

Stop, look, listen!

Sometimes, when we travel down streets, we see signs for interesting things and places to visit and investigate.

When we read, we sometimes see a **question mark** at the end of a sentence. This sign shows us where the sentence stops (.) and that the sentence is a question.

Get set...

Draw a circle around the **question marks** that are drawn correctly.

Put a **question mark** at the end of these sentences.

What is your name

Where are my keys

How much does it cost

Are you hungry

We often use questions to find out information. Draw a line to match each question to the answer that makes most sense. The first one has been done for you.

What time is it?	We got stuck in a traffic jam.
What is your favourite game?	I am six years old.
Why are you late?	I am going shopping.
Where are you going today?	It is 3 o'clock.
How old are you?	I like playing football.

Correct these sentences with either **full stops** or **question marks**.
Draw a circle around the punctuation mark you used.

What time do you go to bed

How did you do in the spelling test

I love going swimming

The kitten played with the wool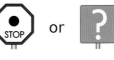

When can you come to play at my house

We need to water the flowers

Can I have more milk, please

Complete the **question** for each of these answers.

What _____

Where _____

How _____

Do _____

My name is Kamil.

I live in London.

I am six years old.

Yes, I have a dog.

Lucas hasn't told Jack if he is coming to his party. Which **question** should Jack ask to find out? Tick the box.

☐ Lucas, do you like eating cake?

☐ Lucas, are you coming to my party?

☐ Lucas, are you going shopping later?

Millie has lost her party invitation. She can't remember when or where Jack's party is. Think of **two questions** she could ask to find out.

1. ....

2. ....

Everybody is looking forward to Jack's party. Complete each sentence with a **full stop** or **question mark**.

I am really excited about Jack's party

Do you think we will play games

What is your favourite party game

I love playing musical bumps

Jack loves balloons

Do you know what Jack's cake is like

I hope it will be a chocolate cake

Sometimes there are warning signs on the road that drivers must look out for. There could be dangers ahead. The driver needs to pay attention and be ready to stop.

In the same way, an **exclamation mark** shows that we must pay special attention to a sentence. We use it to express surprise or anger or when we want to emphasise something.

> This sign shows us both where the sentence stops and that the sentence is an **exclamation**.

Watch out!

Get set...

Put an **exclamation mark** at the end of these sentences.

Come here

Don't run

Oh, no

Stop

Be careful

Be quiet

Go!

Everyone is arriving at Jack's party. They are very excited. Copy the comments into the speech bubbles. Don't forget the **exclamation marks**!

I can't wait!

What a great cake!

Happy Birthday!

I'm so excited!

I love balloons!

Hello!

Write an **exclamation** of your own on the line below.

Go!

The magician is about to start his show. Complete these sentences using **full stops**, **question marks** or **exclamation marks**.

Sit down

I'm still hungry

Quiet please

Do you want to see the magician

Have you got enough room

How does he do it

Yes, please

I think he'll pull a rabbit out of that hat

Commas for lists

A **comma** is like a speed bump on the street. It is there to make you slow down a little bit, to pause and to pay attention.

One way we use **commas** is to separate items in a list.

Sam had fish fingers, chips and peas for tea.

It is important to put the **commas** in the correct place or you could change the meaning of the sentence!

Sam had fish, fingers, chips and peas for tea.

Get set...

Place the missing **commas** in these lists.

William put on his hat coat and scarf.

Kitty had a cheese roll apple and biscuit.

13

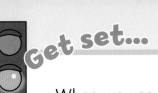

When we use **commas** in a list, we don't have to use 'and' until we get to the last item.

Tom played football with Alex, ~~and~~ Hannah, ~~and~~ Ben and Isaac.

Use the stickers to replace 'and' with **commas** in these lists. Remember the only 'and' you need to keep is the last one.

STICKER TIME!

We went to the shops to buy some bread and milk and apples and bananas and cheese and cucumber and tomatoes.

The ice cream van sells chocolate and vanilla and strawberry and mint choc chip and salted caramel and toffee fudge flavour ice cream.

Complete these sentences by listing three or more items. Remember to use a comma to separate each item.

My favourite things to eat are

On the way to school I go past

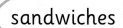

The children are telling their mums and dads about the party. Use the pictures to help you complete each sentence. Remember to use **commas** to separate the items in each list.

sandwiches 　　some grapes 　　and a biscuit

I ate _____

_____

 Emily　　 George　　 and Kamil

I played with _____

_____

 musical statues　　 musical bumps　　and pass the parcel

We played _____

_____

15

 ice cream

 strawberries

jelly

 grapes

and cake

There was

_____

_____

 pulled a rabbit out of his hat

 made the cup disappear

 and found a coin in Jack's ear

The magician

_____

_____

 a balloon animal

 a funny hat

 and a magic set

Jack was given

_____

_____

Stop, look, listen!

Imagine the buildings on a street are words. Now imagine a little person on the roof-top balcony, pointing to something and shouting out "Mine!"

We see the little speech bubble. It looks a bit like a comma in the sky. It is called an **apostrophe**. It shows us when one thing belongs to another.

Lisa's hat   the dog's tail

the baby's bottle

Get set...

Put the **apostrophes** in the right place to show who the object belongs to.

Dads book   Tobys scooter

The cats milk   The teachers pen

My sisters room   My friends mum

Jack's party is over and the children are leaving. Help everyone to go home with the right things by completing these sentences. Don't forget to use the **apostrophe**.

This coat belongs to Katie.

It is _____Katie's_____ coat.

George brought this bag.

It is _____ bag.

These cups belong to the hall.

They are the _____ cups.

This balloon was given to Tom.

It is _____ balloon.

These presents belong to Jack.

They are _____ presents.

The magician used this wand.

It is the _____ wand.

Have you ever seen a demolition ball? Sometimes parts of buildings are knocked down as they are not needed anymore.

An **apostrophe** can be a bit like a demolition ball. It shows that letters are missing and you can zoom on to the end of the word as there are fewer letters to read.

Do not   Don't

I will   I'll

Remember, the **apostrophe** goes where the demolition ball has knocked out the letters.

Put the **apostrophe** in the correct place in these contractions.

I am	→	Im
We will	→	Well
Let us	→	Lets
We are	→	Were

Jack is writing letters to thank people for his birthday presents. Use the stickers to show where he can use **contractions** to make his letter sound more friendly.

STICKER TIME!

Dear Anna

Thank you for the game you gave me for my birthday. We have already enjoyed playing it twice. I hope you will come round to play it with me soon.

Was not the magician at my party great! Mum says he almost did not make it in time because his satnav was not working and he had got lost. He should have had a map too, just in case! I am so glad he called mum to ask for directions.

I can not wait until it is your birthday.

Thanks for being a great friend.

Jack

Lucas is telling his mum about Jack's party. Can you put in all of the missing apostrophes? There are 8 to find.

Remember, you need to use an **apostrophe** to show that something *belongs to* somebody or something, **e.g. mum's** hat.

An **apostrophe** is also used when two words have been contracted to make one word, **e.g. can not** becomes **can't**.

Jacks party was awesome. We played loads of games. I shouldve won musical statues, but I sneezed at the wrong time!

The magicians tricks were amazing. I couldnt work out how he did any of them. It was funny when the magician tripped over Grans bag. Luckily, he wasnt hurt.

Jacks mum made him a fantastic birthday cake. I had so much fun I didnt want the party to end.

Grammar challenge

Can you use what you've learnt in this activity book in your own writing?
Have a go at these challenges and see how well you do.

Challenge 1
Write a full sentence to answer each of these questions. This is a great chance to practise starting a sentence with a capital letter and finishing with a full stop. Remember to use a comma to separate items in a list.

What party games do you like to play?

What party food do you like?

Who would you like to invite to a party?

How well did you do?
- Give yourself one point for each **capital letter** used to start a sentence.
- Give yourself one point for each **full stop** used to finish a sentence.
- Give yourself one point for each **comma** you've used when you've listed more than two things.

Points scored on Challenge 1:

Challenge 2

Follow the lines to match each item to its owner. Then write a short sentence to show who each item belongs to, like this:

Lucy ⟶ 🗝 *It is Lucy's key.*

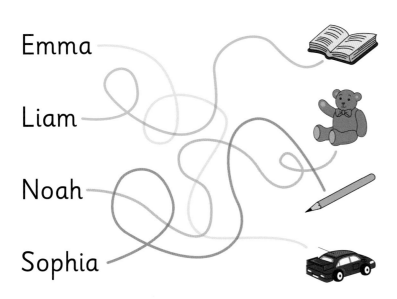

Emma

Liam

Noah

Sophia

How well did you do?
Give yourself one point for each **capital letter**, **full stop** and **apostrophe** you've used correctly.

Points scored on Challenge 2:

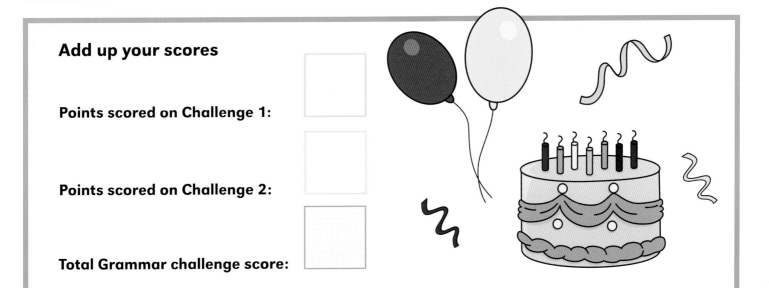

Add up your scores

Points scored on Challenge 1:

Points scored on Challenge 2:

Total Grammar challenge score:

Well done!
Are you pleased with your score?

Sentence punctuation

Give yourself a smiley face sticker for each section of the book you complete.
Look out for the sentence punctuation you've learnt about in this book
when you read. Use it when you write too.

My name is:

I can...

○ recognise that sentences begin with a **capital letter** and end with a **full stop**.

○ recognise **question marks**.

○ recognise **exclamation marks**.

○ understand how to use **commas in a list**.

○ understand how and where to use **possessive apostrophes**.

○ understand how and where to use **apostrophes for contractions**.